A
Darwin
and
Washoe

by

Keiran Proffer

Underhill Management Ltd, London

Published by Underhill Management Ltd,
10 Antrim Mansions, London, NW3 4XT.

First published May, 2002

ISBN 0-9542154-0-0

British Library Cataloguing in Publication Data.
A catalogue record for this book is available from the
British Library.

Printed in Britain by St Edmundsbury Press, Bury St
Edmunds, Suffolk.

Preface

Ever since Darwin wrote "The Origin of Species" in
the 19th century, there has been an apparent conflict
between science and the Bible, especially the book of
Genesis and the origins of man. Modern physics, with its
description of the universe being created in a "big bang"
instead of 7 days has only made things worse. If scripture
is the word of God, then it must be true. But most of
science can be shown to be true, and science says that the
world did not come into existence in the way Genesis
describes. More especially, according to science, God
did not make man out of the dust of the ground as
Genesis says, nor was Eve made from Adam's rib, but
men and women evolved from monkeys, or rather from
ape-like creatures.

Recently chimpanzees and other apes have been taught
sign language and have been seen using tools. The
chimpanzees are using signs in what appears to be
intelligent ways. A talking chimpanzee seems to threaten
our position as unique among the animal kingdom. It
even raises questions about man having souls, because
for centuries Christians have believed that the ability to
speak was the sign of an immortal soul.

Christians have used a number of ways out of this
situation. Fundamentalists have simply retreated into a
complete denial of scientific discoveries. "Scripture is
the word of God and cannot contain any error," they say.
Others try to use all sorts of ingenious arguments to try
to show that the events in Genesis actually occurred.

Others have just stopped thinking about it altogether. Yet others, maybe the majority, treat Genesis as mere legend, with no basis in fact whatsoever.

None of these attitudes is very sensible. God gave us minds and we are meant to use them. Christians have nothing to fear from science, provided it sticks to its own domain. A true Christian can believe in both the Book of Genesis and modern science, provided you view them both in the correct way. This book is an attempt to help today's Christians, and any other reader who may be interested, tackle these problems.

Acknowledgements

Grateful acknowledgement is made for the permission to reprint from several publications which have been listed in the appendix or in footnotes. In some cases all attempts to trace or contact the copyright owner have been unsuccessful. The publisher would be happy to hear from anyone not appropriately acknowledged.

I would like to thank Roger Fouts his assistance, and Richard, Columba, Jonathan and Robert for reviewing the first draft and their helpful criticism.

Also a special word of thanks to the staff of Camden Public Libraries, without whose help I would never have been able either to write this book or publish it.

Contents

Chapter 1

The great fallacy

Talking at cross-purposes is so common that it is surprising how long it takes people to realise that they are doing it. When it comes to science and religion, it seems to be impossible. It is a simple and obvious mistake (or should be obvious!) to assume that both use the word "man" to mean the same thing.

Science defines man as a member of the order Primate, which includes chimpanzees and gorillas as well as other man-like creatures. All these other man-like creatures, like Neanderthal man, are now extinct, except for *Homo sapiens*, or "modern man". Modern man differs from other Primates in that he has an upright posture, an opposable thumb (you can touch the tips of all your fingers with your thumb), a non-opposable big toe (apes can grip with their feet, but men can not), less body hair, a large cranium or skull and several other factors. On the other hand, religion defines man as a creature with an immortal soul. There is no connection between these two definitions. If you look in the book of Genesis you will find no description of what a man looks like. There is no mention of an "upright posture" or "cranial size". When it comes to the difference between man and other animals, science and religion view the whole thing in different ways.

The most important point is that as far as science is concerned, man differs from animals in more than one way. This means, quite simply, that science cannot go back in time and find the "first man". Imagine someone invented a time machine and went back to find the first being with an upright posture, opposable thumb, and so on. This we might say is the first man. But then we find that his brother or his father has a less upright posture and so is not a man, but a larger cranium and so is more of a man! Which one is the first man?

At this point science gives up. When there are *several* characteristics that make up a man, then you cannot draw a sharp dividing line and say, "this was the first man". There can only be a group of beings which at some stage on average have become "men". The same applies to any species of plant or animal. This is why science talks about evolution of populations rather than individuals.

On the other hand, if there is just *one* characteristic that makes man different from the animals, then it is possible to go back to the first man. This is, of course what Christianity teaches: Adam was the first being on this planet with an immortal soul. This means that are far as Christianity is concerned, we can go back to the first man.

Science and religion are not opposed to each other. When they talk about the difference between man and other animals, they are talking about two different things. We can accept evolution of men from monkeys as true, without in any way denying God's special creation of man. Somewhere along the line of evolution was the first man in God's eyes. He may have been very different from what science calls the first man. He could have lived thousands of years before or thousands of years after science's first group of men.

Someone may object that the Bible says God made man from the dust of the earth (Genesis 2:7), and says nothing at all about evolution. These are two good questions.

Scientists believe that the earth was originally without life. Out of what has been called a "hot, thin, soup" of chemicals, that is the early sea, the first cells were made

5

and these eventually evolved into the living things we see today. As scripture puts it, "Let the waters bring forth abundantly the moving creatures that hath life". The "hot, thin, soup" was the early sea, and the chemicals in it were formed by immense electric storms during the early life of the planet. So scientists believe that life, including man, evolved out of inorganic, non-living material. In other words, quite literally, and skipping a few details, man was formed from the dust of the earth.

To see why the details, which we call evolution, were skipped, we will have to turn for help to Sherlock Holmes. As he explained to Dr Watson in *The Sign of Four*, "When you have eliminated the impossible, whatever remains, however improbable, must be the truth". A few minutes thought will show anyone that if evolution did occur, then it would be completely impossible to more than just hint at it in the Bible. There was enough trouble in the 19th century when Darwin published his theory; the reader can imagine for himself what would have happened if someone had presented the same idea 2000 years earlier! Very likely he would have been stoned as a lunatic or heretic. No-one would have believed, or even understood a word of what he said. More important from God's point of view, the real message of Genesis would have been lost. For it must be remembered that it was not God's intention in writing the Bible, to teach men about science.

As I have just said, it was still possible to hint at evolution in the Bible. If the reader looks again at the first chapter of Genesis, he will see that things appear in stages, with man last of all. I think this is as far as God could go to hint at evolution without causing trouble.

Chapter 2

Is scripture literally true?

This chapter is mainly for fundamentalists or any other person who believes that scripture is literally true. Christians believe that the Bible is the word of God. They have different views on what part the human writers of the Bible played, but for the purposes of this booklet we can ignore these. God is Truth, so what the Bible says must be true. Scripture cannot contain any error. From this point of view, it is a small step to saying that the Bible must be literally true throughout.

To reply to this it must first be pointed out that the Bible never makes this claim about itself. Nowhere does it say that scripture is literally true. The New Testament uses the Old in a quite allegorical way. For example Noah's Ark and the flood are referred to as a "type of baptism" in 1 Peter 3:21.

For a Christian there are further problems. Christians believes that Jesus was God, and so Jesus would have to behave like God, or as much like God as a human can do. Yet, we read clearly in the Gospels that Jesus taught in parables (Matthew chapter 13, for example). A parable is a story told to illustrate a point, and nowhere in the gospels does it suggest that any of Jesus' parables actually happened. If there ever was a king who invited guests to a wedding feast and no-one turned up, then no historian has recorded the event! So either Jesus was not God or God teaches in parables.

A second reason why a Christian cannot hold the Bible to be literally true is that Jesus failed to fulfil too many of the Old Testament prophesies about the messiah, that is, if we take these prophesies literally. A couple of examples will do: In the gospel of Matthew 22:44 Jesus quotes Psalm 110 and makes it clear that the "Lord" referred to in verse 1 means him. But then the psalm goes on to say how the Lord will strike people down and fill the world with dead bodies (verse 6). Jesus did nothing of the kind!

The prophesies of Malachi chapters 3 and 4 describe a messiah very different from the Jesus we know who forgave sins and sought out what was lost. The knowledgeable reader will also notice that in these chapters the coming of Elijah before the messiah was prophesied. Taken literally, this did not happen, as you can see from John's gospel (John 1:21), where John the Baptist denies that he is Elijah. However, Jesus says that Elijah did come (Matthew 17:12). So John the Baptist was not literally Elijah, it was not a case of reincarnation, but he had the same type of spirit.

However, it is not necessary to go to the gospels for arguments against scripture being literally true. On the very first page of the Bible it says that the sun was created *after* plants (Gen 1:11,14). There is no way that can be literally true. This is a clear sign from God to all generations against taking the Bible literally. Most men throughout history will have been involved in farming in some way. They would all know instantly that you cannot have plants without sun.

Or if that will not convince you, then go on to the next page. Genesis 2:4 starts off a second account of creation which blatantly contradicts the first (animals are made after man, for example). Go on a bit further and read that Noah's flood lasted both 150 days (Gen 7:24) and 40 days (Gen 8:6). Go on a bit further, and read in Gen 18:21 that God did not know what was going on in Sodom until he came down to earth to see for himself!

Attempts have been made by people throughout history

to reconcile the contradictions in scripture, using every kind of ingenious argument. (Except common sense, of course, as common sense says that if scripture contains two different accounts of something then God is saying, "I am not giving you literal truth here"). My favourite is the statement by some old Jewish authors that the creation of "male and female" in Gen 1:27 means that the original human was hermaphrodite. The creation of woman from man in Gen 2:22 should be understood as the splitting of this original being into two halves. They generally add the comment "and the two halves are permanently trying to get back together again"!

It may be objected that this is God testing our faith and seeing if we will trust His word against science. To this I reply that God does not set difficulties in our way; he wants us to seek him and would make it as easy as possible for us to do so. See for example Jesus denouncing the Pharisees for making the practice of the Law difficult in Mat 23:13 and Luke 11:46. Also the discoveries of science are as much God's word as the Bible. He created both and there can be no contradiction between them. If there seems to be a contradiction, then is it is because we have failed to understand something.

Likewise the belief of some fundamentalists that if science contradicts the Bible then science is simply wrong will not hold water. The discoveries of science can be tested and shown to be correct. If these appear to contradict scripture, then we were taking scripture in the wrong way. In fact one of the functions of science is to tell us which parts of the Bible are literally true and which are not.

One final point: all Christians and Jews accept the concept of "unfolding revelation". God did not reveal his whole message at once, for Christians the teaching of

Christ was the fulfilment of the Old Law. Even in the Old Testament we can see a growth in understanding of God's Law. See for example the change in doctrine about God punishing children for their father's sins in Exodus 20:5 and Ezekiel 18. All people accept a development in the central theme of God's message. Yet for some reason they feel that when it comes to science, God had to be completely accurate from the first.

For the rest of this booklet I assume that the reader has accepted that the Bible can "teach things in parables". If you accept this view you can enjoy the different ways God gets his message across; history, poetry, allegory, fiction, theology and so on. It makes the Bible far more interesting. However, if the reader cannot accept this idea, then I can only ask that you put this booklet down now and go and do something more useful. One last question before you do this: you believe the Bible is the word of God, Muslims believe the Koran is, Hindus believe the Vedas are. Which of you is right?

Chapter 3

A brief summary of evolution

Evolution is now almost universally accepted among biologists. I will not spend much time in going over the proofs. The main ones can be summarised as follows:

1. The existence of fossils shows different plants and animals existed in the past.
2. These fossils show a development into modern forms of animals and plants.
3. The growth of embryos in the womb resembles the evolutionary process.
4. The similarity in groups of plants and animals suggests a common ancestor.
5. The existence of vestiges (like your appendix) points to an earlier organ no longer used.
6. Plants and animals can be changed by selective breeding. Darwin's original work among the finches of the Galapagos islands showed that this also happens in nature.

Evolution is believed to work by two processes: mutation followed by natural selection. A mutation is a change in the genetic material during reproduction, causing the offspring to be different from both its parents. Most mutations are so small that they have no effect. Occasionally a more important mutation occurs, and this affects the offspring's chance of living. The process of "natural selection", or "survival of the fittest" kicks in. If the mutation gives the new creature a better chance of surviving, then it will survive longer than others of its kind. This means it will have more offspring, and these will inherit the mutation. If on the other hand the mutation is in any way disadvantageous, then it will die sooner than others of its kind and so the mutation is lost.

Over a period of time, as more mutations occur, then the species will gradually change. As an example, consider that a long while ago there was a large cat-like animal, living somewhere near the tropics and looking very like a large tabby cat. Some of these big cats lived near jungle and some near grasslands. Those who lived in or near the jungle would have to hunt on their own, as the noise of a whole pack of them moving through the jungle would scare off any prey. Also the ones among them who were stripey would gain an advantage as they would be camouflaged. Gradually the solitary, stripey cats would be selected by the competition for food.

On the other hand, the big cats that lived in the grasslands would be able to hunt in packs, which is a much better way of catching prey. The stripey ones would stand out against the plain back-drop of the grasslands, so the plainer cats would gain an advantage, and these would be the ones who lived longer and produced more offspring. Gradually the two groups would change until eventually they became the two different species we know today, lions and tigers. But there would be no clear point at which the two species began.

That these two species were closely related was shown when a female lion was left in a cage with a male tiger and they produced cubs. Again this shows they had a common ancestor, and that they were not so far apart as people had thought.

It would be wrong, however, to imply that this process of random mutation followed by natural selection has all the answers. In the example just given, it can not answer the fairly obvious question "why does the male lion, alone of all cats, indeed all predators, have a mane?". There seems to be no advantage in having one, or if there is then why are tigers, leopards, wolves and female lions managing quite well without them? Why do lions and tigers have rounded ears, while domestic cats have pointed ears? Why does all the cat family purr? No other creature makes this noise, and the vast majority of animals make no noise at all when they are happy, so what advantage is there in doing it? Also natural selection cannot explain the vast array of different colours found in birds. If there is an advantage for the crow in being black, then why aren't all birds black? In spite of these sorts of questions, it seems that natural selection gives the best overall driving force behind evolution.

The main argument against evolution, apart from the fundamentalists' view that it differs from the Bible, is that though we can see how species can develop, how does evolution explain the arrival of a new organ. Eyes are present in all higher animals. How do you have half an eye?

This is easily answered by looking at more primitive creatures. You cannot have "half an eye", but you can have an area of skin sensitive to light, or rather a group of light-sensitive cells. These over the years can develop into the highly specialised eye we know.

Another argument against evolution is that it seems a bit far-fetched to expect that random mutation followed by natural selection can produce such a wide variety of shapes and forms. How did dinosaurs evolve?

The answer here is that the evolution of dinosaurs, or any group of animals alive today, has taken hundreds or thousands of millions of years. In that space of time, anything could happen. Also, surprisingly, the difference between the genetic structure of species is far smaller than anyone would expect. For example, our DNA is only 1.6% different from chimpanzees. It needs comparatively few changes to produce a new species. (By the way, the fact that 98.4% of our DNA is the same as a chimpanzee's shows that the difference between man and a chimpanzee is not in the DNA).

Now let us apply evolution to man. As with the lion and the tiger, there is no clear point at which a biologist can say, "here the new species begins". If we could go back in time, we would just see men getting smaller, hairier, less upright, less intelligent and so on. There is no way in which science could detect God implanting an immortal soul, and so no way science can mark a dividing line between man and beast, except for two things: only men use tools and only men speak. Unfortunately both of these have been proved wrong.

Chapter 4

Chimpanzees and tool-making

So far I have over-simplified the situation by giving only the biologists' definition of man. Archaeologists, for obvious reasons, define man as a creature who makes and uses tools. In *Man the Tool-maker*, for example, Kenneth Oakley says, "Employment of tools appears to be his chief biological characteristic" (note 1). Archaeologists are, of course, perfectly entitled to define man in this way. There can be as many definitions of man as there are disciplines studying him, and each one can use the definition they find most helpful.

Unfortunately for archaeologists, Jane Goodall discovered in the 1960's that chimpanzees both make and use tools. She spent 4 years by the Gombe Stream in Tanzania studying chimpanzees in the wild - the first time such an attempt had been made - and collected a vast amount of information about the intelligence and complex social life of chimpanzees. The photographs taken by Hugo van Lawick, and published in the National Geographic magazine are so well known that I need not describe them in detail. A chimpanzee can be seen to take a stalk of grass, strip off the side-shoots, and use the bare stalk to probe for termites in a termite mound. Jane Goodall reported chimpanzees going over to a vine to select a suitable branch, stripping the leaves, and using the bare branch for the same purpose (note 2). This shows both forethought and preparation; the chimpanzee has made a tool.

Other examples have come to light as more people have started studying chimpanzees in the wild. Christopher Boesch (note 3) saw chimpanzees using stones to break open nuts. One young chimpanzee was having no effect until her mother took the stone from her, showed her how to do it, and then passed the stone back. The daughter then used the stone in the correct way and managed to open several nuts.

Before this there were several examples of animals using instruments, but none with any sign of intelligence. Sea otters in North America, for example, use rocks to break shellfish. All of these operations can be explained on the basis of instinct; there is no sign of any intelligent preparation of the tool. Obviously this does not apply in the case of the chimpanzees.

Archaeologists have been placed in an awkward position. Do they re-define "man" or do they include chimpanzees as men? Not surprisingly, they have chosen to re-define man as a creature who makes and uses *stone* tools. Kenneth Oakley for example says, "chimpanzees … making simple tools … is a far cry from the systematic making of stone tools, the earliest known examples of which required much premeditation" (note 4). Luckily for archaeologists, grass and wood tools rot away very quickly, and the earliest stone tools were probably so simple that we could not recognise them as tools. Chimpanzees, as just mentioned, use stone tools, but *so far* have not been seen to make any. Let us hope for the sake of archaeologists that this never happens. (I think they are safe. Chimpanzees live largely in trees, and carrying a stone around with them would only be a hindrance.)

On the whole, chimpanzees using tools is not really that disturbing. Archaeologists have simply defined man as a creature who leaves artefacts they can study. This is not really making any statement about what a man is, and their views do not worry either scientists or Christians. A talking chimpanzee is another matter altogether.

Chapter 5

Chimpanzees and sign language

There have been several attempts to teach chimpanzees to speak, ever since they were first recognised as intelligent. All were dismal failures. It was only in the 20th Century that scientists found out that chimpanzees have relatively thin tongues and high larynxes, which make pronouncement of most of the sounds of human speech, vowels and consonants, very difficult. More important, studies of chimpanzees in the wild showed that they were by nature very quiet animals, who only make a noise in special situations, as in warning of danger. In common with most jungle creatures, a noisy chimpanzee would become a dead chimpanzee very quickly.

The breakthrough came when Allen and Beatrice Gardner decide to teach their chimpanzee Washoe American sign language or ASL. (Unfortunately all attempts to create a universal sign language have failed). By the time she was four and a half, Washoe learned 132 signs. This is itself would not have caused much of a stir. We all know that a dog can indicate "I'm hungry" and "I want to go out". What Washoe did that created so much interest was to combine the signs in ways which she had not been taught. For example she signed SUSAN QUIET when she wanted Susan to be quiet. She had been taught the signs for SUSAN and QUIET, but not in that combination. On hearing a barking dog outside she signed LISTEN DOG. Again, she had never been taught to combine LISTEN with DOG. She never made nonsensical signs. One of the longest group of signs she made was GIVE ME SMOKE, SMOKE WASHOE, HURRY GIVE ME SMOKE when begging for a cigarette for the first time. Her teacher signed back ASK POLITELY. Washoe signed PLEASE GIVE ME THAT HOT SMOKE (note 1). (Her teacher, Roger Fouts, responded NO).

In other words Washoe showed that she was using language intelligently, and not just repeating what she had heard, like a parrot does. Linguists regard the use of combination of words in ways that you have not been taught as the essence of language. By signing LISTEN DOG, Washoe showed that she had understood the general concept "listen" and the general concept "dog". She had no difficulty in understanding that the sign TREE referred to all trees. This was shown beyond all doubt when Washoe started recognising pictures of things she knew and make the signs for them. In fact one of her favourite past-times was leafing through a picture-book and making signs for the things she recognised - just like a human child. Washoe learned the signs for BANANA and APPLE, but also the signs FOOD and DRINK, showing she could understand the concept of classes of objects.

After a time Washoe started generating her own signs for things when she had not been taught. A refrigerator she called OPEN FOOD DRINK, having been shown these 3 signs separately. This was despite her teachers calling it COLD BOX. As the sign language manual her teachers were using did not have the sign for BIB, Washoe invented her own - drawing the outline of a bib on her chest. The Gardners insisted that she use the sign for NAPKIN, which was in the manual, and eventually she did this. Later on they found out that she was using the correct ASL sign for BIB, but as this is drawing the outline of a bib on your chest, the coincidence is not too surprising. What is most significant is that Washoe had invented a totally new sign for something; she had invented a word. This shows some degree of creativity and the intelligent use of language.

Since the work of the Gardners was published there have been a number of other attempts to teach chimpanzees and gorillas sign language. All report the same: combining signs in ways that they have not been shown, and creation of signs to point to things they did not know. The gorilla Koko referred to another gorilla, Michael, as TOILET DEVIL. When told about this, Michael signed STINK BAD SQUASH GORILLA LIP (note 2). Their teacher did certainly not teach them these groupings. The chimpanzee Lucy, taught by Roger Fouts, called a radish CRY HURT FOOD, showing that she had grasped the three concepts "cry", "hurt" and "food", and also that she has more sensitive taste-buds than the author of this booklet. Chimpanzees and gorillas who had been taught ASL used it among themselves when there were no humans present, and have been filmed doing so from hidden cameras by the Gardners' team.

Ally, a male chimpanzee, was tested by Roger Fouts for comprehension of grammar. When asked where something was he showed that he could understand FLOWER ON PILLOW and BALL IN BOX. Ally sometimes confused his locations, but he always signed subject-preposition-location in the correct order. He knew the difference between TOOTHBRUSH ON BLANKET and BLANKET ON TOOTHBRUSH (note 3). He apparently had managed to learn the basic rules of grammar along with the signs.

Washoe eventually came to know over 1,000 signs. Standard English consists of 600 words. She was later given an orphan chimpanzee to raise. Loulis, the young chimpanzee, learned sign language from Washoe and Ally. Exactly like a human child, ninety percent of his signs were by imitating his parents, but in a few cases Washoe was seen to teach him a sign (note 4). This was done both by repeating the sign to the young chimpanzee, or by moulding Loulis's hands into the sign.

Now that they know what to look for, naturalists are beginning to report the use of language by chimpanzees in the wild. Toshisada Nishida describes different courtship gestures used by different tribes of chimpanzees, quite close to each other geographically (note 5). Up to now, it was believed that all animals in the wild used only in-built forms of communication. That is, they should be the same the world round. Konrad Lorenz remarks in the classic *King Solomon's Ring*, published just after the Second World War, "Animals do not possess a language in the true sense of the world... I heard the jackdaws in northern Russia 'talk' exactly the same familiar 'dialect' as my birds at home in Altenburg [Austria]" (note 6). This plainly does not apply to chimpanzees.

Chapter 6

Reactions to Washoe

The Gardner's work has placed linguists in the same position as archaeologists. They now have to include chimpanzees as men or re-define "language". This is a lot more serious than chimpanzees using tools, because of a simple equation which has been assumed by linguists and philosophers for the last three centuries:

language = thought = reason = human uniqueness.

I should explain that there is also an enormous amount of prejudice to be overcome. Ever since Descartes described animals as mere machines, scientists have followed this belief almost without question. Any attempt to describe animals as thinking or feeling emotions has been dismissed as "anthropomorphism". It is taking many years and repeated observations of animals to disprove this.

Furthermore, linguists mainly follow the teaching of Noam Chomsky, who believes that humans have a language facility, or something like a "language organ" somewhere in their mind-brain set-up. This enables them to speak and use grammar, two abilities which are so complex that they could not be learned in the normal way. This language organ is believed to exist only in humans, in other words we are "pre-programmed" to learn language. As apes do not use language, they cannot have this language organ. (I should mention that so far dissection of the human brain has not revealed any such organ, and it has not been described by psychiatrists).

So the immediate reaction for linguists is to deny sign-language in chimpanzees altogether. There have been mistakes in the past, where intelligence was falsely attributed to animals. The most famous case was that of Clever Hans, a horse who lived at the turn of the previous century. Trained by his owner to answer questions in arithmetic by tapping the answer with his hoof, Hans amazed everyone by not only giving the correct answers to questions like "what is the square root of 16?", but answering questions written on boards! An investigating panel including two zoologists and a psychologist was formed in 1904, and could find nothing wrong. It was only later that a young psychologist found that Hans only gave the correct answer when his owner knew it. When the horse was fitted with blinkers, or when the board was held up so the questioner could not see it, then Hans just tapped away without stopping. What Hans was doing was responding to the small, involuntary movements his owner made as he reached the correct number (note 1).

Part of the trouble with Clever Hans was that there was no fraud involved. His owner genuinely believed he had taught Hans arithmetic, and was shocked and disappointed at the discovery. Hans has left his legacy, because scientists have ever since been very wary of attributing any form of intelligence to animals. It is also a warning against self-delusion, which is of course the charge that has been labelled against the Gardners. Most people will over-exaggerate the intelligence of their pets, and it is true that the people working with Washoe, Ally and Lucy did get emotionally involved with them. This is still no grounds for questioning their findings, which were subject to rigorous tests by the scientists themselves (note 2). Also it is worth noting that if they had not built up a relationship with their pupils, they would probably have been able to teach them very little.

Now to details of the denials: Some linguists tried denying that sign language was language at all, but in view of the number of deaf and dumb signers throughout the world, this objection collapsed at once. Then some sign language speakers observed the chimpanzees and questioned whether some of the signs were correct signs at all. Here there is a genuine difficulty: in a (British) sign language manual you will find that the sign for "man" is to stroke the face with thumb and fingers, to indicate a beard. The author of this booklet learned this sign himself, and was surprised when he saw a deaf man signing with what was a just quick flick of the hand towards the face. Men and apes who use sign language of course speak it much faster and with less emphasis than a novice does. This does make interpretation very difficult; did the chimpanzee really sign, or just move his hands vaguely? The Gardner's had got to know Washoe very well over the years, and so they could recognise as sign which would be invisible to a new-comer.

Another attack has come from the fact that when subject to a series of tests, chimpanzees gave the correct signs only 77% of the time. Here unfortunately we come up against the fact that we are dealing with a living being rather than a machine. Too often when presented with an object the chimpanzee will simply run off and play with it. Or they will get bored with a repetitive test. However, 77% is far more than chance would allow, and better than a two year old human would get (see Chapter 7).

A far more serious challenge came from psychologist Herbert Terrace who repeated the Gardner's experiments with a chimpanzee named Nim at Columbia University. From the beginning Terrace wondered if the chimpanzees were simply associating hand signals with food items, like Pavlov's dogs with a bell. This question was answered when Nim created his own signs for HAND CREAM and PLAY. Also Nim used the signs for ANGRY and BITE, which as Terrace pointed out was the only example of any non-human species substituting and arbitrary word for a physical action (note 3). Terrace then objected that Nim often started signing before the questioner had finished. "Children show a good sense of when to listen and when to talk", he said (note 4). He obviously has never tried to talk to the children in the flat below me! More seriously, signing together is quite usual among the deaf and dumb, as you can read signs while signing yourself, as opposed to speech where it is difficult to talk and listen at the same time.

But the crucial objection came from the extensive videos Terrace had taken of Nim and his teachers signing to each other. Terrace divided Nim's signs into five categories: spontaneous, imitation, reduction, expansion, and novel (note 5). Spontaneous signs were originated by Nim; the rest were in response to a teacher. A reduction was an imitation with some signs missing, an expansion was an imitation with some additions, and novel signs had no overlap with the teacher's signs. Terrace was able to show that only 10% of the time Nim made spontaneous signs. About 40% of Nim's signs were imitations or reductions. When he later reviewed the films made by the Gardners of their chimpanzees signing, Terrace pointed out that the same thing was happening: the chimpanzee was simply responding to signs from the humans.

The results of project Nim were seized on by linguists and it was widely trumpeted that the Gardners had been proved wrong. However, I must ask to reader to look at the figures just quoted. Nim did not respond to human signs 100% of the time, but 90%. 10% of his sign were spontaneous. 40% of the time he made imitations or reductions, which means that 50% of his signs were expansions or novel signs. Nim was not *just* responding. Also of course, the Gardner's film was made with the purpose of showing a chimp signing, so they prompted the chimps as much as possible. It was not a record of their training sessions.

More important, it turned out that Terrace had used an approach that encouraged Nim to do nothing but respond. He had used a reward and punishment method, which was already known to be *not* the method children use to learn language. Children, and the Gardner's apes, learn language in the same way: by babbling at first to their parents and siblings, and then learning to imitate their elders. When Nim reached for anything he wanted the teacher withheld it, moulded the object's sign, and then asked Nim to sign for it. When he did make the sign, he was given the item. "I wanted Nim to learn to sign in order to please his teachers", Terrace says in his book (note 6). Terrace had deliberately chosen an approach which would prevent the chimpanzee learning in the way children learn to speak. Worse, Nim was taught by no less than sixty teachers in succession, which prevented him building up a secure relationship with any of them. As Terrace admitted in the closing chapter of his book, Nim only gave spontaneous signs with people he liked and trusted.

All these considerations did not prevent the scientists declaring that the whole idea of apes talking was a fraud. The final nail in the coffin came when Terrace and others published a paper in the journal Science entitled "*Can an Ape Create a Sentence?*" . As the paper said, all linguists accept that "using human language indicates a knowledge of grammar". It then reviewed the Nim project, saying, "There is no evidence of an ape's ability to use grammar". The paper concluded, "There is no evidence that apes can combine symbols to create new meanings. The functions of the symbols of an ape's vocabulary appears to be not so much to identify things or convey information as it is to satisfy a demand that it use the symbol in order to obtain some reward" (note 7). In short, Nim was doing exactly what he had been trained to do.

It may be that, given time, the opinion of the linguists would have changed as more and more evidence of chimpanzees and gorillas using sign language among themselves, when there is no chance of human prompting, were recorded. But that will always remain an academic question. While all this was going on a quite different experiment in animal communication was being conducted with a female pygmy chimpanzee. Nobody paid much attention to the baby she was carrying on her back, but he was about to upset the whole apple-cart.

Chapter 7

Chimpanzees and symbols

Sue Savage-Rumbaugh of Georgia State University approached the whole question of ape language with an attitude of healthy scepticism, having had severe doubts about the demonstrations she saw of chimpanzees making signs (note 1). She set herself the difficult task of proving one way or another whether chimpanzees really understood the meaning of the signs they were using. To do this she used a computer based on the Yerkish language developed to help severely retarded children. A touch-sensitive screen is used to display a set of arbitrary symbols, and the computer can record when a symbol, or lexigram, is pressed. So unlike sign language, there is no question of whether the symbol has been pressed or not. There was no need for videos; the computer recorded it all. There was no clue in the facial expression or body language of the computer what the sign might mean. Finally, to prevent the chimpanzees learning the positions of the symbols, the screen was re-arranged after each use.

By a series of carefully designed tests and a lot of trial and error, Savage-Rumbaugh was able to show that the two male chimpanzees she was working with, Sherman and Austin, could learn very quickly that pressing a particular symbol produced a particular food. It took further training to get them to select the correct symbol for a food item when they knew they were not going to receive it, and some time before they could grasp that someone else pressing a symbol was trying to communicate something to them. When they had understood this, they were put into separate rooms with an observation window and a hatch between them. They could ask each other to pass over a food item, which they did. They were then given a completely new food item. The reader who remembers Washoe and Nim will have no difficulty predicting what happened. The chimps at once selected an unallocated symbol, and used it for that food item from then on. One fact has been proved beyond all doubt: if a chimpanzee learns any form of sign language, it can invent new signs without difficulty.

More inventive tests involving tools, or the chimpanzees having to tell each other what was hidden in a container, were passed with ease. They had reached what Savage-Rumbaugh had identified as the final level of understanding of language, that is realising that the other person does not have some information you possess, and trying to communicate it to them. The crunch came when Austin had to sign to Sherman that there was peanut butter in a container, which Austin had seen filled but Sherman had not. Austin went to the keyboard, only to find it turned off. He immediately picked up a label off a peanut butter jar, and held it up for Sherman to see. Sherman stared at it for a moment and then pressed the symbol for peanut butter.

Tests on assigning things to the general categories "food" and "tool", once they had learned these symbols were again passed with almost 100% accuracy. (Apparently the researchers had not heard about Washoe's ease in applying "tree" to all trees, or maybe they doubted it.) In the final test, of assigning the *symbols* of food and tools into categories, Sherman scored 15 out of 16, and Austin 17 out of 17 (note 2). As far as seems possible, Savage-Rumbaugh has shown that apes can understand the symbols they use.

Having had a resounding success with Sherman and Austin, Savage-Rumbaugh started a new project with a female bonobo called Matata. Bonobos, or pygmy chimpanzees as they have been called up to now, are still relatively unknown in the West. This is partly because they are restricted to the Zaire (Congo) river basin, and also that they were only recognised as a separate species in 1933. In fact their bone structure is quite different from the common chimpanzee, in many ways similar to early man. Their social structure, as far as is known, is far less aggressive and male-dominated than the chimpanzee, which makes them much easier to work with. Even the friendly Sherman and Austin started fighting at times, and as an adult male chimpanzee is as strong as three grown men, chimpanzee fights are not something to be taken lightly.

Matata, who from the start of the project carried her adopted son Kanzi on her back, bonobo-style, had shown early signs of intelligence. It was therefore with frustration and annoyance that the researchers found the whole project a failure. After two years of training Matata had learned only six symbols, and only at the first level of "if I press this sign I will get a banana". Things were not helped by Kanzi playing with the keyboard, and Matata's refusal to let anyone discipline him. Eventually, Matata was sent back for a breeding program, and they decided to try again with Kanzi. The only explanation that Savage-Rumbaugh could give for the failure was that Matata was ten years old when the project started. This is older than any chimpanzee or gorilla who has been tested for any form of language. In the light of later research, this explanation is probably correct.

The day after Matata's departure the keyboard was set up for Kanzi to start his training. On that first day he keyed in APPLE and CHASE, then giving his teacher a big play grin, picked up an apple and ran off with it. He then went on to use the keyboard 120 times and showed that he understood at least eight symbols. "I was hesitant to believe what I was seeing", wrote Savage-Rumbaugh (note 3). Just by riding on his mother's back and watching what was going on Kanzi had learned more than his mother had achieved in two years. He had just demonstrated what had been talked about all the way through, but no-one had had the courage to put into practice: chimpanzees learn language in the same way human children learn, by simple exposure to it. This meant, among other things, that Nim's 60 teachers had been an expensive waste of time. Nim would have learned better if he had simply been left with a deaf or dumb family. As soon as Kanzi's teachers realised this, they abandoned any attempt at formal training. Kanzi was given a stimulating environment in which to learn, with as many games as possible. Within four months he knew more than twenty Yerkish symbols.

Kanzi started combining symbols in his first month, and unlike Nim, 90% of his combinations were spontaneous. As he added more elements the information content increased, as with ICE WATER GO when asking someone to get some iced water for him, as opposed to Nim's simple repetitions.

There were more surprises to come. When Kanzi was one and a half years old someone noticed that when they mentioned light, Kanzi went over to the light switch and flipped it off and on. A brief test showed that he understood at least 35 English words. Sherman and Austin given the same test showed no comprehension of spoken English at all. Once again Kanzi had started to learn a language by simple exposure. By the end of the 17-month trial period, Kanzi could understand 150 English words as well as lexigrams. He had effectively become bi-lingual. The research team was reduced to spelling out anything they did not want him to understand. Even then he appeared to be listening very carefully.

When Sue Savage-Rumbaugh tried to publish the results of the work with Sherman and Austin, she met such rejection that she was warned about the difficulty she was likely to face if she tried to report on Kanzi's achievement. It was only after several attempts that she could find a journal willing to publish it at all. The scientific establishment had been frightened off by the Nim experiment.

The team set up a test to see how well Kanzi could understand spoken English; Kanzi was now seven and a half years old. They selected 660 sentences which they thought Kanzi had not heard before. This meant using some bizarre phrases like "wash the hot dogs", but on the whole Kanzi could comprehend them. The questioner was hidden behind a screen, to prevent any clues from the posture, and the recorder sat in the same room as Kanzi, wearing earphones to prevent him hearing the question. The same test was given to Alia, the daughter of one of the researchers, who was two years old. Kanzi scored 74%, a figure very close to Washoe's 77% in a similar test, while Alia scored 65%. Kanzi's grasp of English was better than a two-year old child's. (A later experiment in learning lexigrams compared Kanzi's half-sister Panbanisha with a common chimpanzee showed the bonobo was always ahead in learning and comprehension).

An analysis of the computer's records of Kanzi's combinations of symbols by Patricia Greenfield showed that in his first month Kanzi used PEANUT HIDE as often as HIDE PEANUT, but this very rapidly became

HIDE PEANUT every time. Kanzi was putting the action first and the object second. This he probably picked up from spoken English, where the object follows the verb. On the other hand, if he wanted someone to do something, Kanzi gave the action lexigram first, then indicated the person with a gesture. This is the opposite of English, where the subject comes first. Where he used two verbs, as in TICKLE BITE (a game Kanzi invented), they were most frequently used in the order in which they were to occur. Kanzi was using a rudimentary grammar.

Chapter 8

Are apes really using language?

To sum up, between them Washoe, Sherman, Austin and Kanzi have covered just about every definition of language it is possible to make: using words, inventing words, using categories, passing every test for comprehension which could be devised, learning in the same way as humans, and using simple grammar. Linguists are placed in a far worse position than archaeologists. They have responded by either wildly denying or by re-defining language. Noam Chomsky in an interview for the New York Times said, "Humans can fly about 30 feet - that's what they do at the Olympics. Is that flying? The question is totally meaningless. In fact the analogy to flying is misleading, because when humans fly 30 feet, the organs they're using are homologous to the ones that chickens and eagles use. Whatever chimps are doing is not even homologous as far as we know" (note 1). Herbert Terrace quoted earlier, insisted that the chimpanzees were not using language as their signs or symbols did not develop into full sentences.

Of course, some will always claim that apes are not really using language at all, just that they have a conditioned response to associate a sign with an object. All one can say about this belief is that it is not based on any fact or observation. Pigeons can be trained to peck a particular key when shown an object, but they have to be trained to do it. No pigeon ever taught himself to do this, as Kanzi did. Also, present a pigeon with a new object, and he will not know what to do. Sherman and Austin at once selected a new symbol, and used it consistently from then on.

Given that apes have demonstrated an understanding of language equivalent to a two to three year old child, it is not possible to ask them, "exactly what do you mean by that symbol?". However, here is a summary of the observations made which imply apes do understand language:

1. Stringing together signs in ways they have not been taught (all chimps and gorillas mentioned).
2. Invention of new signs for new objects or ideas (a) by combining two or more known signs (Washoe), and (b) by inventing a totally new sign (Nim, Sherman and Austin).
3. Use of signs to inform or request from another person, and comprehending that the use of the same sign by another person was doing the same (Sherman and Austin).
4. Understanding of categories, such as "food" and "tree" (Washoe, Sherman and Austin).
5. Search for alternative ways of communicating the information if the usual way was not available (Sherman and Austin).
6. Learning language in the same way as humans (Kanzi).
7. Using simple grammar (Ally, Kanzi).
8. Teaching language to their children (Washoe and Loulis).

This is the situation at the time of writing. All the facts are on the side of those who claim that apes can use language. Against them are just denials and the Nim project, which could be described as a successful experiment in *not* teaching sign language. The denials will wear out in time. The requirement that apes create sentences is probably safe for the moment, as it is clear that they have roughly the same grasp of language as a two to three year old child. This is just before the child starts to form full sentences. Also how anyone develops a full sentence using symbols or sign language, has never been specified.

Before we leave this section I will make two final observations. All the work carried out so far has been teaching apes English. Modern English is only some eight-hundred year old, and full of peculiarities. Fortunately no ape was subjected to the horrors of English spelling. One of the unusual characteristics of English is that the word order in sentences is important. "John loves Mary" has a quite different meaning from "Mary loves John", as opposed to say classical Greek where word order is irrelevant. North American linguists are of course going to look for English syntax in apes signing. What would happen to an ape exposed to a more primitive dialect, we must wait and see.

The second is that all the apes tested so far have shown roughly similar levels of intelligence, except maybe for Matata, who may have been more stupid than most. When Washoe's achievements were first published, some scientists tried to claim that she was a freak. This has now been shown to be false, but it has also been shown that apes differ widely in personality much as humans do, and so presumably in intelligence. Every so often, mankind throws up someone who is remarkably more intelligent than his fellows. What happens if we stumble across a chimpanzee Einstein?

Chapter 9

The Christian response

Any linguistic philosopher who has read so far will probably be muttering to himself something like "kettle calling the pot black", or maybe "take the beam out of your own eye". The response of Christians to talking apes has been the same wild denial or to look the other way and try to pretend that it hasn't happened (note 1). The reason is quite simple. Christians are working off the same equation as linguists, though with a slight addition:

language = thought = reason = human uniqueness = immortal soul.

Archaeologists can hide behind the fact apes do not make stone tools, and linguists can hide behind the fact that apes using sign language do not construct complete grammatical sentences; but the rest of mankind knows this is just hair-splitting. Faced with a talking, tool-making chimpanzee, Christians have three choices. Either apes have immortal souls, or more realistically apes have the beginning of language and hence the beginning of souls and souls evolved, or language is not the outward sign of an immortal soul.

The idea that apes have immortal souls forms no part of Christian tradition, and one we find very difficult to take seriously. However, it is being implied in some way by the movements that have been started to give apes the same rights as humans (note 2). At the time of writing there is the serious possibility that Australia may adopt this into its law.

The main objection to this is that it is extremely unlikely that God would give a soul to an animal that was incapable of giving due expression to it. In spite of their ability to communicate, there is no indication that any ape could praise God or understand the gospel.

The second idea, that apes have the beginning of souls and that souls evolved, has a lot more to be said for it. The belief that souls are inherited from your parents has been put forward by some Christian thinkers, Tertullian for one. (For something to evolve it must be passed on from generation to generation, and so must be inherited from your parents.) However, the Catholic Church soundly condemned this view (note 3), and as far as I know no Christian group today holds to it. It also defies ordinary common sense; how could something immortal, eternal evolve from time? (Note: during the middle ages, animals were regarded as having animal souls but this need not detain us. In modern terms, "soul" means immortal soul.)

So finally we have to come to the conclusion that equating language and reason with an immortal soul is wrong. This equation has been assumed by Christians for centuries, and it is easy to see why. Man is the most intelligent animal on this planet and is also the only one with an immortal soul (at least as far as we know). It is obvious that everyone would assume the two things went together. Yet as soon as it is questioned the assumption falls apart. Could God give an immortal soul to a tree? Of course, all things are possible to God, but for the reasons mentioned earlier it is very unlikely that he would do so. A tree could have a soul, but it would be unable to express it, having no brain and no intelligence. Or could God make a being as intelligent as man, and not give it a soul? Again the answer must be yes, though again it is doubtful if he would do such a thing.

The problem is that ever since the Greek philosophers,

especially Plato, man has been regarded as being a duality of body and soul. Hence, for example Christ's use of "body and soul" to describe the whole man, as in "fear him which is able to destroy both soul and body in hell" (Matt 10:28). This meant that animals had to be pure body, as only man has a soul. Animals could have instincts which controlled their behaviour, but nothing like reason, which was unique to man. That this was a totally false assumption has now been demonstrated by the mass of information we have accumulated about the intelligence of great apes, a mass which is growing daily. If we try to keep to man as a duality of body and soul, then we get into increasingly difficult situations. When humans create a new word from two existing ones, like "lawn-mower" or "*unter-see-boot*", then it is the use of man's reason. When Washoe coined "open-food-drink" for refrigerator then it was brute instinct! We cannot keep this attitude up for much longer.

In fact the whole problem has been solved for us by the ordinary man in the street, who never took the slightest notice of the idea of a body-soul duality. In the nearest large bookshop to me is a section dedicated to health, the paranormal and religion. It is entitled "Body, Mind and Spirit". "Spirit" is used to mean the same as "soul". To the ordinary man in the street, Man is a trinity.

First, to any Christian it is most fitting that man should be a trinity rather than a duality, for obvious reasons. (There is a limit to how far this analogy can be pushed, of course. God is a trinity of persons making one God. Man is a trinity of body, mind and soul making one person.) Second, this view of man answers all the problems. The body we know we share with all animals, and especially with the great apes. The mind can be allowed to evolve, and can have functions like language and thought that we share with apes and with earlier versions of man. The uniqueness of the human soul or spirit is preserved. Third, there is some support for this view of man in scripture, as for example in Christ's statement, "Thou shalt love the Lord thy God with all thy heart, and with all thy soul, and with all thy mind" (Matt 22:37). This shows that mind and soul can be distinguished. Finally, a look at any writing where the author described man as "body and soul", will show that "soul" and "mind" are used interchangeably. All mental, social and emotional faculties are lumped together under either "soul" or "mind". This was acceptable when the abilities of great apes were unknown, but now we must start to distinguish between the two.

Chapter 10

Soul and mind

At this point someone may object that speech could not have evolved, as scripture says, "Adam named the beasts" (Gen 2:19-20), and so Adam was the first one to speak.

I will agree that this interpretation can be put on these sentences, but a close examination will show that this means something quite different. Throughout the Old Testament to know the name of something - its genuine name - meant that you could summon it and control it. Hence the angels refusal to reveal their names to men (Gen 32:27, Judges 13:18), and the awful taboo against pronouncing the name of God. This idea is still present in the New Testament, where in Revelations 2:17 the saved are given a name known only to themselves. This means that from then on they are free of all domination by other people, and that they have complete control over themselves. Fallen nature is restored. So Adam naming the beasts is a statement of Man's superiority over the rest of God's creation, and that all animals were originally subject to him. It does not mean that Adam was the first speaking being on this planet.

So in this booklet I am presenting mind and speech as two things that evolved together along with the body, particularly the brain, whereas the soul was a direct creation from God. Mind is inherited from parents, with all its reasoning powers and inherited behaviour patterns. Obviously it is also modified by personal experience. There are two questions here: how does mind relate to the brain, and what is the difference between mind and soul?

Just to review the question of how mind relates to the

brain would turn this short book into an encyclopaedia. Luckily is not really relevant to our subject. I will just make a couple of observations:

First, no-one has ever proved that we use the brain for thinking. It is obvious that the brain is associated with intelligence to some degree; this is shown by comparing the sizes of various animal brains. But beyond that no-one has gone, largely I think because no-one can define exactly what thinking is. However, for the purpose of this booklet, I will assume that the brain is at least involved with intelligence.

Second, or perhaps following on from that, no-one has ever shown the relation of even the most basic mental functions with the electronic and/or chemical functions of brain cells. Looking down at my carpet I can see the colour red. How do you get from an electronic impulse to the sensation of *redness*? Or, as Roger Fouts pointed out, even a robin, a bird with a small brain, has to have within it the general principle "how to catch a worm", otherwise it would starve to death. Moreover, this general principle must be modified each day to catch this particular worm, and expanded as the robin becomes more experienced in worm-catching, or changed if the robin moves to an area where there are few worms, and has to make do with grubs instead. How do you get from an electro-chemical impulse to a general principle? Even the most hardened materialists, those who deny the existence of mind at all, cannot begin to answer this question.

The question of the difference between mind to soul will take more working out. I assume that all mental functions that can be observed in animals to some degree are functions of mind, and anything truly unique to man is the result of man possessing a soul. What has become clear in the late 20th century is that many of the things that had been though to be uniquely human are in fact held in common with animals, or at least our closest relatives among them. Language is just the latest discovery. Science and philosophy, as we understand them today, are not found in animals, but as these have only been around for about 2,500 years they cannot be called characteristic of man either. On the other hand, chimpanzees will pull a thing apart to find out what it is made of. That is perhaps the essence of science.

Language and tool-making we have already covered. Chimpanzee paintings have been known ever since Desmond Morris carried out his televised experiments with the chimpanzee Congo in the 1950's. The new dimension that signing chimps added to their paintings was that when asked they could say what it was meant to be. (The painting of a bird published in an English newspaper in the 1970's was especially good.) When an art critic was shown Ally's paintings for the first time, without being told whom they were by, he was enthusiastic. "I knew Pollack was coming back", he said (note 1). In other words, chimpanzees can paint just like modern artists, or modern artists paint just like chimpanzees, depending on your point of view. Either way, art cannot be considered a unique human attribute.

The complex structure of chimpanzee societies is only just being uncovered, due to the pioneering work of Jane Goodall in Africa, and Frans de Waal in Arnhem zoo. Both of them found that chimpanzees form groups or tribes, and within that group they form friendships, trade with each other, deceive each other, play with each other, and settle disputes - sometimes by appealing to a third party. Even the naïve assumption that the strongest male would become the dominant, or "alpha" male has been shown to be wrong. A weaker male who can muster more support from other members of the group, including females, will topple an alpha male. Chimpanzee politics is a case of factions, in-groups, pressure groups and alliances (note 2).

At the end of his survey, Frans de Waal was driven to say, "In their social application of reason and thought, chimpanzees are truly remarkable. Technically their inventiveness is clearly inferior to human beings, but socially I would hesitate to make such a claim" (note 3). So politics and other social activities, including votes for women, are found in apes.

It has become clear to me, and probably to the reader, that I have taken the wrong approach here. I am going to have to give up this attempt to list all the ways in which the mind of man resembles the other primates, or this book will literally never end, as more information on this subject is published every day. It will be easier to approach it from the other side, by consideration of the soul.

But first, I have to relate one example of deceiving others which we will have occasion to refer to later. Danny, one of the smaller males of the Arnhem zoo community, and hence of fairly low rank, was also the most intelligent. The keepers noticed that whenever a group of chimpanzees escaped from their enclosure, Danny was always one of the party. When some grapefruits were hidden in the chimpanzee enclosure all the chimpanzees, Danny included, ran past the place where they were hidden. While the others were having an afternoon siesta, Danny went back to the place alone and dug up the grapefruit. Had the others been with him the more high-ranking males would have taken most of the fruit from him (note 4).

Deceiving others involves an understanding that you

have some knowledge that they do not. This means that a chimpanzee must be aware of his own mind to some extent, and aware of others. Christians and scientists for centuries having been denying this awareness could exist in any animal except man.

They also have been shown to attack and kill chimpanzees in other tribes. Jane Goodall, who first observed this behaviour, commented that this was due to "a unique combination of strong affiliative bonds between adult males on the one hand and an unusually hostile and aggressive attitude towards non-group individuals on the other" (note 5). So even war is not a uniquely human invention. Now let us look at the human soul.

Chapter 11

The human soul

The functions of the soul, as distinct from the mind, appear to be two-fold: it is aware of itself, and it is designed to love God and neighbour. With the information we now have on animal behaviour, both of these are going to be difficult to disentangle from animal minds.

Self-awareness I define as a function of the soul based on God revealing his name as "I am" to Moses (Ex 3:14), and that man is made in the image of God (Gen 1:27). So I would expect genuine self-awareness to be a function only of human beings. Proving this is not going to be easy. First it is impossible to prove that someone else is or is not self-aware. When it comes to proving this across species, it is going to be virtually impossible. The facts, such as they are, are these: Gordon Gallup first tried painting a red dot on the foreheads of some chimpanzees while they were asleep. When they later saw themselves in a mirror, the chimpanzees started feeling their foreheads to see what the red dots were (note 1). Sue Savage-Rumbaugh's chimpanzees and bonobos reacted in various ways to their image in the mirror, but all of them seemed to recognise that it was their own image. Panbanisha used the mirror daily to examine her growing canine teeth. Washoe, when asked "who is that" about her reflection signed ME WASHOE.

When Washoe's baby died she seemed able to understand what had happened. When one of he teachers had a miscarriage, Washoe signed CRY to her. Koko the gorilla understood when she was told that her pet cat had been killed in a car accident, and cried over it. When later asked about the cat she signed BLIND SLEEP

45

CAT. So it seems that apes can understand death.

Chimpanzees seem also to be able to understand that they are chimpanzees. Any animal brought up in the company of another species assumes that it is a member of the same species, due to a process called "imprinting" discovered by Konrad Lorenz (note 2). When first introduced to other chimpanzees, Washoe called them BLACK BUGS. She later settled down to mixing happily with them. Ally, on the other hand, appeared to have a nervous breakdown when he realised that he was not a man as he had thought, but one of these strange, black, hairy creatures (note 3).

If chimpanzees are aware of their bodies, aware of what kind of animal they are, and can understand death, then what extra awareness is given by the soul? The answer must be in the two questions that human children ask, the first about the age of 7, "Where did I come from?, and then, "What is life all about?", during adolescence usually. True self-awareness is to be aware of our existence and that we exist for a purpose.

The question of what would justify baptising a chimpanzee has been given several answers. If we follow the logic of the 18th-century cardinal seeing an orang-utan for the first time, "Speak, and I shall baptise thee", then we must baptise Washoe. In the 20th century the theologian F J Sheed said, "If one ever met a pig capable of knowing it was a pig it might be safer to baptise it" (note 4). Again this would mean that Ally would have to be baptised. My own conclusion is that if a chimpanzee ever signalled "Where did I (or we) come from?" or "Why was I born?", or something similar, then we would have to baptise it, as these questions show true self-awareness. There is just one reservation about this. When she was pregnant, Washoe did seem to understand that she was carrying a baby inside her (note 5). Maybe a straight *physical* question about where they came from would not justify baptism.

Once established, true self-awareness can spill over into other fields. An intelligent animal can easily invent and use a language, but only a true man can ask "What is language?; What is its function and purpose?; Why do we have grammar?", and so on. In short, only a man can step back and analyse things.

The second function of the soul seems to be to love God and neighbour. No animal can do either of these things. Now the reader will be able at once to think of occasions in his experience, or a story he has heard, of some great self-sacrifice or act of devotion by an animal, usually a dog for its master. This has been explained as a combination of pack loyalty to his leader, and the instinctive love of a young mammal for its parent (note 6). I am sorry to disillusion the sentimental reader, but it is something purely natural. Any social animal must have friendly feelings towards other members of his group, or the species will rapidly wipe itself out. This does not stop chimpanzees from stealing from each other, or cheating each other - as with Danny and the hidden grapefruit. An animal can see nothing wrong with coveting his neighbour's ox, but God expected men to understand the command forbidding it.

When we move outside the group or tribe, the animal instincts of friendship break down. I have already referred to the fact that chimpanzees will kill members of other tribes. So obviously will men. As I write this the world is still recovering from the effects of tribal warfare in Rawanda and Yugoslavia; the latter being more shocking as it took place in a supposedly "civilised" European country. All moves to end the fighting between Israeli Jews and Palestinian Arabs have failed. No animal, or man who just follows his animal instincts, could understand the command not to oppress the stranger among you, and above all no animal could ever understand or practise the command "love your enemies".

Love of neighbour is of course the second commandment. We were made to love God. It is not possible to imagine an animal, however intelligent, contemplating and adoring God, for the simple reason there is no evolutionary process which could bring this about. The driving force in evolution is believed to be survival of the fittest. How this could bring about a self-less love of God no-one can explain. Also the love of God leads us into behaviour which goes clean against our instincts for survival and production of offspring. It is hard to imagine an animal taking a vow of virginity, or being prepared to suffer torture or martyrdom for his beliefs. Conversely no animal would kill another because of its beliefs.

The love of the God we cannot see with our physical eyes, nor understand with our animal intellects, spills over into other areas. Only a true man is capable of dedicating his life to some invisible cause - truth, justice, democracy, or even a new form of art, and so on. Probably the pursuit of justice is the most common result of man having a soul. An intelligent animal could pass laws, but they would only reflect his own interest, or what we call today "political solutions" to problems. Only a true man could pass a law against his own interest on the basis of a commitment to a system of justice. In the *Euthyphro*, Plato imagines Socrates questioning a young man who has come to the law courts to have his father arrested for murder. Of course the philosopher, using his pagan intellect, could not understand why anyone would want to do such a thing. Our intellects can no more understand the activities of our souls than our bodies can sense the activities of our intellects; you cannot see with your physical eyes the difference between two ideas.

Chapter 12

Do whales have souls?

Earlier I referred to the fact that man is the most intelligent being on this planet and the only one with an immortal soul. I then added, "as far as we know". Off-hand I can think of one folk-tale and three science-fiction stories in which man is revealed not to be the most intelligent animal on this planet. Douglas Adams's book and radio series, "The Hitch-Hikers Guide to the Galaxy", in which it turns out that mice are the most intelligent beings, is merely one of the best and funniest of these. Usually it turns out that cats are the most intelligent, for obvious reasons: all food provided, never being asked to do any work, and so on.

Humans are intelligent monkeys and we can never escape this fact. Our perception of the world and of God is limited by our ancestry. When we praise God it is as intelligent monkeys. Some aspects of God must remain hidden from us, aspects that an intelligent, spiritual crab, for example, would understand at once. If God is to be praised fully in this creation, then somewhere in this universe there must be an intelligent crab praising him. Also an intelligent fish, bird, amphibian and possibly all other types of creature, so that the whole of the created universe can ring with the praise of all aspects of God which creation can understand.

On this earth, apart from the jokes, there is only one other animal that can seriously be considered as intelligent and spiritual. Sperm whales have brains that are larger than humans', which is at least an indication of intelligence (note 1). Also their brains have the same convoluted folds as human brains. Apart from that we know very little about their behaviour and intelligence, due to the obvious difficulty in studying them in the wild or captivity. Dolphins we know have roughly the same intelligence as chimpanzees; could whales relate to dolphins as we do to chimpanzees?

The philosopher Wittgenstein made a famous comment, "If a lion could talk, we could not understand him". This we now know is wrong. We can understand the sign language of chimpanzees. I can also understand the smaller, domestic version of a lion who is living with me. (She also understands me well enough, including the word "no", it is just that she leaves it for a while, and then tries again later.) When it comes to whales Wittgenstein may have been correct. We have recorded and analysed hours of whale songs, and argument is still raging whether it is territory marking, sonar tracking, or genuine communication. This is hardly surprising given the completely different way of life that they have. Whales never manipulate any physical object, they are living in an environment where they can move in all three dimensions, they must come to the surface to breathe, but they spend most of their time below it. There really does seem to be very little we have in common. If whales are communicating then it is possible that we will never understand them.

There the matter would rest if it were not for an intriguing line in Genesis: "and God created great whales" (Gen 1:21). As I make no claim to be a biblical scholar, I will quote the theologian F.J.Sheed directly: "'In the beginning God *created* the heavens and the earth'. The verb 'created' is not used again except for *man* (whose soul is in fact a fresh creation) and *whales* (if there is any significance in this I do not know what it is). With these two exceptions, the verb used is 'made'" (note 2). That is, once the universe of space, time, matter and energy was created, all other things were made from it, including the body of man. Apparently mind, if we accept that chimpanzees have minds, is also part of this universe. So why is the verb "created" used for whales? Is this because whales have immortal souls just like men?

Conclusion: until this matter is cleared up, whaling had better cease. Apart from the extinction of a beautiful creature, we may be committing the further crime of killing a fellow spiritual being.

Chapter 13

Adam

Men and apes diverged around 4-8 million years ago. During this time man's forerunners developed in intelligence and culture until they were far ahead of the chimpanzees and bonobos we see today. Even at a late stage they were not considered to be modern men, *Homo sapiens*, until about a quarter of a million years ago. From a Christian point of view, by the time the first true men, that is creatures with souls appeared, the hominids could have had an exceedingly high level of culture.

I am going to use the word "hominid" to describe a creature that is very close to being a man, but does not have a soul. This is slightly different from the scientific use, which uses "hominid" for all types of men, but I cannot at the moment think of a better term. Where I use the term "man" or "true man", I mean a being with a soul.

So the hominid mind evolved to the point where it was capable of giving expression to an immortal soul. At this point God had two options, either he could start infusing souls into all children that were born to hominids, or he could infuse a soul into one individual and his descendants. Adam, in other words, was either one man or a group.

Adam as a group, or as just a term meaning "man", has been put forward in the early part of the 20th century when the full meaning of the theory of evolution began to dawn on Christian theologians. However, what they were doing was equating Adam with the species *Homo sapiens*, which as I hope I have shown in chapter 3, was a mistake. It was a view condemned by Pope Pius XII in 1950, though in rather cautious terms: "the faithful cannot lend support to a theory which involves either the existence on this earth, after Adam, of true men who would not originate from him, as the ancestor of all, by natural generation, or that 'Adam' stands for a plurality of ancestors. For it is not apparent how such a view can be reconciled with the data which the sources of revealed truth and the documents of the Church propose concerning original sin, namely, that it originates from a sin truly committed by one Adam, is transmitted to all through generation" (note 1). In other words, if someone could show that Adam as a group could be reconciled with Christian dogma, then the objections would disappear. I do not know of anyone who has even suggested how to do this.

We can also add a few further objections to the idea of Adam as a group: the story in Genesis is clearly written with one man as the main figure. I did hear a priest once try to claim the story was originally written with Adam as a group, but on questioning he could not give any clear arguments to support this view. I should mention that Genesis chapter 1 describes God creating man "male and female he created *them*". But this is so vague, that it cannot be used as an argument. Also the first part of the same verse says, "in the image of God he created *him*". In the New Testament, it is clear that Adam was regarded by St Paul as one man, for example: "as by one man sin entered into the world.." (Rom 5:12). Also of course the second Adam, Christ, was one man and not a group. Even in biological terms, the idea of Adam being a group is not sound. For Christians there is one single difference between a man and a hominid. As I said in chapter 2, if there is a single feature distinguishing one species from another then you can look for an individual with that feature.

The clinching argument is the Christian doctrine of the Fall. Mankind's evil behaviour on this planet can be explained reasonable well as that of a chimpanzee or something similar with a large brain. As we have seen, cheating, stealing, wars and murder occur in chimpanzee communities. It is a matter of revelation, and basic Christian doctrine, that this was not the original condition of man. When Adam first existed he was created in a condition of friendship with God and the ability to control his animal nature. It was due to his disobedience that the friendship with God was broken and human nature became disordered. Hence we lost control of our passions, and had to be redeemed. If Adam was a single individual then the inheritance of a fallen nature from him makes sense. If Adam was a group, then either some members of the group did not sin, and so there are some races of humanity which do not have fallen natures, or the entire group sinned. There is no sign of any race on earth being morally superior to any other; the arrogant assumption of the white races in the 19th century has been disproved by the Nazis. For the whole of mankind to have taken part in the original sin, then this would have to include babies and children in the womb, which again makes no sense.

To recap: I suggest that Adam, the first single being with a soul, was born into a community of hominids, and that all his descendants had souls, and so possession of souls spread throughout the race of hominids, until all were true men. For this to happen true men had to inter-breed with hominids. This may sound unnatural to the reader, but it is the normal way for a mutation to spread throughout a species. Also physically and intellectually hominids may have been indistinguishable from men. There is of course no obligation on God to create a soul for every child born of one soul-bearing parent, but I cannot think of any reason why he should not do this.

There may be an explanation here of the odd passage in Genesis chapter 6: "The sons of God saw the daughters of men that they were fair; and they took them wives of all which they chose". It is usually taken that this is a remnant of an old legend, and that the "sons of God" are some sort of angelic being, or even visitors from outer space. Perhaps it is better understood if the "sons of God" were true men, and the "daughters of men" were in fact hominids. So this verse in scripture is describing the inter-breeding of men and hominids.

Chapter 14

Adam's descendants

The reader may have noticed already that there is one serious objection to the picture I have described: it raises the possibility of hominids being alive today, that is creatures who look like men but are not in fact descended from Adam, and do not have human souls. This is a very valid objection, and it will take some time to answer it. First, I must point out that there is nothing in scripture or Christian tradition against this belief. When Pope Pius XII condemned the view that the human race had multiple origins, he condemned the belief of the existence of "true men who would not originate from [Adam]" (note 1). Note the use of the words "true men". It says nothing about the possible existence of hominids today.

However, I do not think that there are any hominids alive today, for the simple reason that it would be a physical near-impossibility. When I described the mating of a true man or woman with a hominid, I said that the result would always be a soul-bearing child. If this happened, and I cannot think of any reason why it should not, then very rapidly the whole of the human race would consist of true men. Only the natural level there is no mutation so dominant that it would automatically appear in all descendants of the first parent. In order for a group of hominids to be alive today, they would have had to keep themselves in total isolation from the rest of mankind from the very beginning. Given the nomadic nature of early man, this is extremely improbable.

Just to take one example: probably the most isolated group of men are the aborigines who colonised Australia about 50,000 BC (note 2). (America was colonised much later, around 15,000 BC). In order for aborigines to be hominids (and there is no justification in such a belief), then their ancestors must have been hominids, and there must have been no contact between aborigines and the rest of mankind during the whole 50,000 years until the arrival of Captain Cook's expedition. In other words, the crossing to Australia was made by a group of people 50,000 years ago and never repeated. What unique event in the world's history caused this crossing, so unusual that it never happened again? And why did no Polynesian fisherman ever get blown off course and washed up on an Australian beach, or whatever?

Even if we do accept the extreme view that there was no such contact, then the whole picture falls apart if the aborigines were true men when they arrived in Australia. This would mean that Adam lived some time before 50,000 years ago. I cannot see any objection to this, except from Christian fundamentalists.

Incidentally, I am assuming along with the rest of mankind that Adam lived somewhere in the Middle East, probably in what is now Israel. This is a reasonable assumption, but one that has never been proved. If the reader tries to find the location of the Garden of Eden from the rivers named in Genesis chapter 2 (11-14), he will find that they give a meaningless position. The Bible might just as well have said "east of the moon and west of the sun". It is at least conceivable that Adam was an Australian aborigine, and the contact had to go the other way.

If the reader will bear with me, I will take another approach to the spread of true men. In 1650 bishop Ussher made his famous attempt to find the date of creation by working backwards through the Bible, taking all ages of the patriarchs as literally true. As is well known, he fixed the date of creation as 4004 BC. What is less well known is that his dating of the births of the patriarchs agrees very well with archaeology back as far as Abraham. Interestingly, the Bible itself changes tone at the call of Abraham in Genesis chapter 12 from mythological language into a brisk narrative style.

Taking Abraham as the first point in the Bible which can be dated with a historical certainty, we find that Abraham lived around 2000 BC. If we assume that a man has 2 parents, 4 grandparents, 8 great-grandparents and so on, and that a new generation comes every 25 years, then by the time we have worked back 1000 years, Abraham had more ancestors than there were people alive. This means that he was related to everyone else on this planet. To allow for duplication of ancestors (as occurs when cousins get married), and to allow time for people to move around the world, and to be on the safe side, we can double this figure. This comes out to the interesting result that Adam could have lived around 4000BC. If Adam lived in 4000 BC, then by the time of Abraham everyone on this earth who looked like a man, was a true man. There were no hominids left.

This may mean a couple of stories in the Genesis are more true than a lot of modern scholars would have you believe. The story of Noah's flood describes the whole of mankind except Noah and his family being wiped out. There have been several major floods in the Middle East, but archaeology does not know of a flood covering the whole earth. If at the time of the Flood, true men had not spread from the Middle East, then the whole of mankind - that is true men not hominids - could have been wiped out by a comparatively local flood.

The story of the Tower of Babel, and God confusing the tongues of men, could also have a basis in truth. It may represent the dispersal of true men among the tribes of hominids on this planet. A similar dispersal occurred among the Jews many centuries later. As they were dispersed, they would come to pick up the languages of the tribes they settled in, and so the race of true men which originally spoke one language started speaking a multitude of tongues.

Chapter 15

Adam's father

So Adam was born into a tribe of hominids somewhere between 50,000 BC and 4000 BC, though I must admit I favour the later date. This means that he had a mother and father. Both of these were hominids, but we can assume that God selected the parents of the first Adam as carefully as those of the second. They were both, obviously members of *Homo sapiens*, as the last Neanderthal died in Europe around 35,000 BC. They had died out in Africa and the Middle East long before that.

Let me make a side-comment: If we take the Genesis story of Adam being made from a handful of dust literally, then God had to implant in him all the things that humans learn during their childhood: how to walk, speak, eat and so on. It would be much simpler from God's point of view to have him brought up in the normal way, with parents who could teach him all these things. It does less violence to nature. Furthermore, Adam could not turn on God and demand to know why he never had a child-hood or parents like every other living thing. End of side-comment.

Adam's parents would have been very intelligent, loving and supportive beings. In their tribe - I am guessing that Adam's father was the chief - all arts would have flourished. Even building could have been quite advanced; this was the period when people were beginning to live in cities. Adam's father would have been famous for settling disputes among his people, and maybe even among neighbouring tribes. In battle he would have been a courageous fighter and a skilful tactician, so that other tribes learned very quickly not to attack them, but that friendly relations were rewarded.

What language did they speak? We do not know, and it does not really matter. There have been some ill-judged attempts in the past to bring up children isolated from all human contact, in order to find out what language Adam spoke. The children always wind up unable to speak at all. There are no grounds for assuming that Adam spoke Hebrew, which is a quite advanced language. Also there is no real justification for assuming that Adam spoke some universal or perfect language. People who teach this seem to be basing it on the line in Genesis in which Adam named the beasts. We have already covered this. Adam's parents and Adam would just have spoken the language of their tribe.

Now the reader may have noticed that when I talked of cultural affairs belonging to the mind, and so could be shared with chimpanzees, there was one glaring omission. What was Adam's father's religion? Adam's father did not have a soul, and so would not have asked any of the fundamental questions about his existence, nor would he have understood the concepts of love of God and love of neighbour. Take these out of religion and what do you get left with? Answer: an awful lot. Most pagan religions would be completely unchanged. Ritual, ceremony, tales about Gods and heroes, theology, hierarchy - all of these can be practised without the two things central. Even in advanced religions like Judaism one can study the law in detail, making it a purely *intellectual* exercise with no mention of justice - as Christ accused the Pharisees of doing (Mt 23:23-26). Everyone knows someone who's Christianity is a mere matter of external observance. (Perhaps this is getting less common now, as being a Christian is not necessary for social status).

Adam's father then may well have had some sort of

religion, but it would have been in the form of legends about former heroes of the tribe - they would not yet have been elevated into god status. There would have been rituals practised at the change of seasons and when members of the tribe were born, married or died. There may have been some concept of "another reality" experienced in dreams. In short, nothing that could lead Adam into error.

Having said all that, their son must have been something of a puzzle to Adam's parents. One can imagine Adam's father settling a case where a weak man (i.e. hominid) had had his land seized by a stronger one. When he found that the weaker man could only farm half the land anyway, Adam's father ordered the stronger man to return half of it. He was very surprised when Adam took him aside afterwards and said that all the land should have been returned, as it was not right for the stronger to steal from the weak. Adam's father was puzzled: both parties had gone away happy, the stronger man had gained some land, and the weaker man, who had been afraid he would lose the lot, had got back all he could use. What was all this talk about right and wrong?

Then there was Adam's habit of going off alone in the evening, and when asked what he had been doing replied, "Talking with God". His parents could make nothing of that at all.

What was even more puzzling was that as Adam grew up he refused to marry any of the girls they selected as a wife for him. But this subject needs a chapter to itself.

Chapter 16

Eve

"And Adam gave names to all cattle, and to the fowl of the air, and to every beasts of the field; but for Adam there was not found an help meet for him. And the Lord God caused a deep sleep to fall upon Adam, and he slept: and he took one of his ribs, and closed up the flesh instead thereof. And the rib, which the Lord God had taken from the man, made he a woman and brought her unto the man." (Genesis 2:20-22).

Throughout most of man's history a mixture of legend, fact, moralising, theory and so on would be the norm in any book, especially one that was about life in general. It was acceptable for someone like Euclid to write a book on mathematics, or Aristotle one on logic, but these were the exceptions. Normal literature should be a mixture of everything; hence for example Dante's great poem *The Divine Comedy* contains a description of a straight forward experiment in physics using candles and mirrors (note 1). Also for most man's history both the author and the reader knew what they knew and what they did not know, the stock of knowledge being much less than today. In general terms this still applies. If I write a book entitled "The animals of Japan" then the reader will expect a factual book. If the title is "The animals of Fairyland" he will expect something quite different.

So the vast majority of readers of Genesis would have no problem about a story about how God made the first woman out of one of Adam's ribs. He would know perfectly well that the writer was just inventing. It was only centuries later that those born into a different culture would demand that it all be taken as literal truth.

The writer of the story in Genesis has lumped together

two quite different events. The first was the naming of the beasts; we have discussed this earlier. The second was the attempt to find a help meet for Adam. There is no sense in God trying to mate Adam with a female wolf or hippopotamus. He must have been looking among the female hominids.

By the laws of inheritance which I have sketched out, Adam should have married a female hominid, and so the race of true men would have been established. An old legend tells of Adam asking God for a wife, and I think this is probably true. Though he could easily have married a female hominid, he would never had much in common with her. The female hominids could talk about boyfriends, parties, dressing up, marriage, raising a family and so on; all of which Adam was quite prepared to join in. The trouble was they could never go beyond this. If he ever tried to talk about the things that really mattered to him, he was met with blank incomprehension. Adam wanted a true woman for his wife.

Rather than try to make sense of the story in Genesis, let us look at it from the other side. Adam was now about twenty years old, and ready to marry. God had to get a real woman from somewhere. Being God, who found the world he had made "very good", he would want to do the least amount of disruption to the created order. The simplest approach was to take a female hominid of Adam's age and breathe a human soul into her.

There is a widespread belief that the Catholic Church teaches that the human soul is infused into an embryo at the moment of conception. This has never been solemnly defined. The truth is that the Church does not know at what point a soul enters an embryo. However, any Christian thinker in the past who has declared that the

soul is infused into a growing child at some later date -
some have even suggested after birth - has never been
able to give the slightest reason for his belief. To be on
the safe side, the Church assumes that the soul is present
from the first. Doctrines like the virginal conception of
Christ and the immaculate conception of the Virgin Mary
imply this anyway. Whatever the views of Christians,
no-one (as far as I know) has ever suggested the soul
enters the body at eighteen years old. So putting a human
soul into a grown female hominid was a change from the
usual procedure, but the one that caused the least
violation to the created order possible. For Eve it must
have been as if she suddenly woke up after being asleep
for sixteen years. All at once she became aware that she
was alive, and that fascinating things were going on all
around her.

If we assume that Eve was a member of Adam's tribe
then the expression "Adam's rib" begins to make sense.
The Christian Church is called "Christ's body" by St
Paul (1 Cor 12:27); his tribe could be called "Adam's
body". So Adam's rib was a female member of Adam's
tribe. Perhaps Adam's tribe was a large one, maybe a city
or a group of loosely-connected villages. Anyway they
eventually met and for the first time Adam found
someone who could understand him.

Later came the Fall. The fact that the tree was present
in the garden shows that God intended man to eat the
fruit eventually, but not at that time or in that way. It is
going outside the scope of this book, but I will make a
brief plea for justice for the memory of Eve. She has
been blamed for the fall by generations of men, starting
with Adam himself. In fact if the reader looks at the story
in Genesis carefully, he will see that Eve was not present
when God told Adam not to eat of the tree, so she must

have heard it second hand. Maybe Adam did not make it clear enough. Then she was tempted by the devil, the master tempter, and resisted at first. There is no sign that Adam resisted at all. Finally their eyes were only opened when Adam ate the fruit. If Adam had said no, it would have just been the sin of one woman and not the whole race.

When their son Cain grew up, he married a female hominid. Cain had a fallen nature, and the bonds of love between man and wife had been damaged. He no longer cared if he had a real relationship with his wife. The cities that the Bible tells of in the later verses, such as the one Cain's son Enoch lived in, were cities of hominids (Gen 4:17).

Chapter 17

Death and the mind

I have left this chapter to last, as it is the most speculative. As this booklet has said repeatedly, man is composed of body, mind and soul; mind consisting of all our thoughts and feeling that cannot be ascribed to the activity of the soul. What happens to the body when we die cannot be doubted; we can see it decompose. What happens to the soul is a matter of revelation; Christ told us that it departs ultimately to heaven or hell. But what happens to the mind?

My first reaction to this question was to treat it like the question "What happens to the music when you turn the record-player off?". Mental activities appear to be produced by the brain. When life ceases to flow through the brain, mental activities just cease, like light vanishing from a light-bulb when the light switch is flipped. There is, however, evidence to suggest that this is too simple a view.

As I suggested earlier, there is far more to the mind than can be explained by a physical brain. There seems to be no way to get from a physical electro-chemical effect to a mental concept. This means that in principle at least it must be possible for some parts of the mind to exist separate from the body. At least this can be conceived as happening. Some medium, as yet unrecognised by science, must be capable of holding thoughts and other mental activities.

This is of course all speculation. There may be evidence, if the reader will accept it, in the activities of spiritualists and psychics. That is people who claim to be able sense the presence of dead people, and pass on messages from the dead to the living, or who can take hold of an object belonging to a person and tell you something about that person, even though they have never seen them. Probably no area of human activity is more subject to fraud and deception. However, the author's personal experience in this field has convinced him that there is an element in it which cannot be explained away. It seems that something of a dead person is left behind, often associated with a place or physical object, and a sensitive person can detect this. We know what has happened to the soul and the body; this implies that the psychic is having some sort of contact with the remains of the mind of the dead person. If it is associated with a particular place, then the place is what we call "haunted". This often seems to be connected with an occasion when powerful emotions were released; that is a murder or suicide.

I suggest that the mind decays in much the same way that the body does. With no soul to hold it together, it breaks up into a mass of disconnected thoughts and feelings inhabiting some medium which is connected to the physical world. Eventually these thoughts disperse and fade away. When a psychic gives what she calls a message from a dead person, she is picking up one or more of these thoughts. All volition is supplied by the psychic; there is no consciousness behind the message. So people who attend spiritualist séances are being misled, not intentionally most of the time, but they are still chasing shadows.

Chapter 18

Conclusion

The great apes are our nearest living relatives, or so science continually assures us, and men evolved from something similar to today's chimpanzees. If this is true, then it would be quite incredible if there were no indications of at least the beginning of human characteristics in our ape cousins. The surprise is that it has taken so long for men to find this out.

The discovery that we can teach language to apes is one of the most exciting of the 20th century. At last we can make some sort of meaningful communication with another species. We can gain great insights into how thought and language evolved; as it is obvious that evolve is what they did. Against this is only the fundamentalist view of scripture, or the now out-of-date view of animals as mere machines. What is most puzzling is that this view is held most firmly by atheist philosophers and scientists. How exactly thinking, reasoning, speaking man evolved from mere machines, they never try to explain. That this happened in only 4 million years is another problem they do not seem to want to tackle. Four million years is a very short time in evolutionary terms. Yet according to linguists, the "language organ" evolved from nothing in that short space of time. The only way this could happen would be by the direct intervention of God!

For Christians, once we understand that soul and mind are two different things, then there are no great problems. The Bible was written for all men at all times. To expect a 20th-century scientific account of creation is completely unreasonable. It would mean nothing to a man born 1,000 years ago; and quite possibly mean nothing to a man born 1,000 years from now. We nearly all recognise that God in Genesis was not trying to teach man scientific fact, rather that he used images and metaphors. Even so, as I hope this booklet has pointed out, a lot of Genesis, far more than has been thought, is in fact either literal truth, or truth dressed up in parables to make it acceptable.

Appendix: What do you do with a talking chimpanzee?

At the end of the project, Lucy was sent to Africa in an ill-judged attempt to adapt her to jungle living. As she had never lived in the wild she had to be helped at every stage by a woman who luckily knew sign language. Eventually she did manage to live in a semi-wild state, but was killed by human poachers. She had no fear of humans and may have approached them herself.

The Oklahoma University announced that all the chimpanzees were to be sold to a biomedical laboratory called LEMSIP. Roger Fouts visited this place and found that they were to be housed in solitary cages the size of small cupboards. They could see each other across the room, but no physical contact was possible. There was no daylight, as the labs had no windows. The cages were empty with steel gratings at the bottom down through which the chimp's faeces would drop on to plastic trays. The labs were not interested in giving the chimpanzees any entertainment: they were there to provide blood for testing and no other purpose.

After a battle that nearly wrecked his professional and personal career, Roger Fouts managed to save Washoe and three other chimps. Eventually he was able to set up a home for them, but it was always touch and go as far as money was concerned. Looking after an intelligent chimp is expensive.

The other chimpanzees were sold to LEMSIP. Visitors to the labs said they saw them signing to the technicians, asking for food, drinks, cigarettes, or the keys to their cages. Of course, the technicians knew no sign language. Fortunately, the story leaked out into the press, and there was an uproar. The two most famous, Nim and Ally were returned to the University. This caused the complaints to die down, and no other signing chimps were returned. The Fund For Animals bought Nim and he went to live on a ranch with a female companion. Ally was not so lucky. He was sold to another laboratory in New Mexico. Roger Fouts could never find out officially what happened to him, but unofficially he heard that Ally had been injected with insecticide as part of a study, and had died as a result.

Jane Goodall wrote an article for the New York Times ("Prisoners of Science", 17 May 1987), describing the conditions in which chimpanzees are held in laboratories in the USA. This caused another uproar, and the battle lines were drawn between those who regard chimpanzees as sensitive, social beings, and those who regard them as useful laboratory tools. This battle is still going on. Interested readers can check the web site www.geocities.com/rainforest/vines/4451 for details.

Notes to chapters

Chapter 4
1. Kenneth Oakley, *Man the Tool-Maker*, introduction.
2. Jane Goodall, *In the Shadow of Man*, chapter 3, p35ff.
3. Quoted in *Next of Kin* by Roger Fouts, chapter 4, p76f.
4. Kenneth Oakley, *Man the Tool-Maker*, introduction.

Chapter 5
1. Roger Fouts, *Next of Kin*, chapter 5, p98.
2. Francine Patterson and Eugene Linden, *The Education of Koko*, chapter 18.
3. Roger Fouts, *Next of Kin*, chapter 7, p159.
4. *ibid*. chapter 10, p235.
5. Toshisada Nishida, "Local Traditions and Cultural Transmission", *Primate Societies*.
6. Konrad Lorenz, *King Solomon's Ring*, Chapter 8, p76f.

Chapter 6
1. For a brief review of Clever Hans see www.thoemmes.com/psych/pfungst.html.
2. Roger Fouts, *Next of Kin*, chapter 7, p157ff.
3. Herbert Terrace, *Nim*, chapter 10, p150.
4. *ibid*. chapter 13, p219.
5. *ibid*. chapter 13, p215ff.
6. *ibid*. chapter 5, p52.
7. Reprinted with permission from Science 206, 891. Copyright 1979 American Association for the Advancement of Science.

Chapter 7
1. Sue Savage-Rumbaugh and Roger Lewin, *Kanzi*, chapter 1, p6ff.
2. *ibid*. chapter 3, p89.
3. *ibid*. chapter 5, p135.

Chapter 8
1. New York Times June 6, 1995. Quoted here by kind permission of Professor Chomsky.

Chapter 9
1. See web site www.probe.org/docs/search.html for example, or www.creationscience.com under "languages".
2. www.greatapeproject.org/gapfaq.html
3. Neuner and Depuis, *The Christian Faith*, n407

Chapter 10
1. Roger Fouts, *Next of Kin*, chapter 7, p156.
2. Frans de Waal, *Chimpanzee Politics*, chapter 1, p43ff.
3. *ibid*. Introduction.
4. *ibid*. chapter 1, p51.
5. Jane Goodall, *The Chimpanzees of Gombe*, chapter 17, p534.

Chapter 11
1. Sue Savage-Rumbaugh and Roger Lewin, *Kanzi*, chapter 1, p20.
2. Konrad Lorenz, *King Solomon's Ring*, chapter 11.
3. Roger Fouts, *Next of Kin*, chapter 7, p169.
4. F J Sheed, *Theology and Sanity*, chapter 12.
5. Roger Fouts, *Next of Kin*, chapter 9, p214.

6. Konrad Lorenz, *King Solomon's Ring*, chapter 10, p118ff. See also *Man Meets Dog* by the same author.

Chapter 12
1. S M Minasian etc, *The World's Whales*, chapter 3
2. F J Sheed, *Theology and Sanity*, chapter 10.

Chapter 13
1. Neuner and Depuis, *The Christian Faith*, n420

Chapter 14
1. Neuner and Depuis, *The Christian Faith*, n420.
2. Chris Scarre, *Timelines of the Ancient World*, chapter 4.

Chapter 16
1. Dante, *The Divine Comedy*, Paradise, canto 2.

References

Main references (in suggested reading order):

1. Konrad Lorenz, *King Solomon's Ring*,
   Methuen & Co., London 1952.
2. Jane Goodall, *In the Shadow of Man*, revised edition,
   Orion Books, London 1988.
3. Roger Fouts, *Next of Kin*,
   Michael Joseph, London 1997.
4. Frans de Waal, *Chimpanzee Politics*,
   Jonathan Cape, London 1982.
5. Herbert S. Terrace, *Nim*,
   Eyre Methuen, London 1980.
6. Herbert Terrace et al, *Can an Ape Create a Sentence*,
   Science, Nov 1979.
7. Sue Savage-Rumbaugh and Roger Lewin, *Kanzi*,
   Doubleday, London 1994.

Web sites used:

1. www.creationscience.com
2. www.geocities.com/rainforest/vines/4451
3. www.gorilla.org
4. www.greatapeproject.org/gapfaq.html
5. www.paws.org
6. www.probe.org/docs/search.html
7. www.thoemmes.com/psych/pfungst.html
8. www.cwu.edu/~cwuchci/main.html

Adam, Darwin and Washoe

Other books consulted:

1. All scripture quotes from the Revised Version.
2. Douglas Adams, *The Hitch-Hikers Guide to the Galaxy*, Pan Books, London 1979.
3. Dante, *The Divine Comedy*, trans Dorothy L Sayers, Penguin Books, London 1949.
4. Allen and Beatrix Gardner, *Teaching Sign Language to Chimpanzees,* State University of New York Press 1989.
5. Jane Goodall, *The Chimpanzees of Gombe*, Harvard University Press, London 1986.
6. Konrad Lorenz, *Man Meets Dog*, Methuen, London 1977.
7. S M Minasian etc, *The World's Whales*, Smithsonian Books, Washington 1984.
8. Neuner and Depuis, *The Christian Faith*, Collins, London 1983.
9. Toshisada Nishida, "Local Traditions and Cultural Transmission", *Primate Societies*, ed B.B. Smuts, Chicago University Press 1987.
10. Kenneth Oakley, *Man the Tool-Maker,* British Museum (Natural History), London 1975.
11. Francine Patterson and Eugene Linden, *The Education of Koko*, Holt, Rinehart and Winston, New York 1981.
12. Chris Scarre, *Timelines of the Ancient World*, Dorling Kindersley, London 1993.
13. F J Sheed, *Theology and Sanity*, Sheed & Ward, London 1978.